D1072342

If found, please contact:

_____

_____

Reward:

_____

The
FIVE MINUTE
JOURNAL

The simplest, most effective thing you
can do every day to be happier.

Intelligent
Change

intelligentchange.com

Intelligent Change

GET IN TOUCH
hello@intelligentchange.com

BE A STOCKIST
partner@intelligentchange.com

CREATED BY
Alex Ikonn & UJ Ramdas

DIRECTOR
Mimi Ikonn

Published by Intelligent Change.
Original edition ISBN 978-0-9918462-0-7

Printed in China
on 100% recycled paper
certified by the FSC®
Lot 100028

FSC
www.fsc.org

RECYCLED
Paper made from
recycled material

FSC® C074709

intelligentchange.com

To lifelong learners and doers.
You're changing the world
every day.

Those who don't believe in magic will *never find it*.

ROALD DAHL

The Five Minute Journal is not a magic pill.
Although, there is certainly some magic at work here.
You still have to do the work in the real world.

Get out of your comfort zone.
Take action and make magic happen.
This journal is your guide.

You are ready.

Contents

Five Reasons

You Will

Love

The Five Minute

Journal

1. IT'S THE SIMPLEST THING YOU CAN DO TO BE HAPPIER.

It's been proven over and over again that shifting your focus to the positive can dramatically improve your happiness. The key is consistency. With a positive quote every day, a weekly challenge, and a structure to help you focus on what's good, you will find The Five Minute Journal to be a great way to start and end the day.

2. IT'S BUILT ON PROVEN PSYCHOLOGY.

Somehow, it took psychologists about 80 years to realize that it's better to focus on positive behavioral traits as opposed to depression, anxiety, and disorders. This journal spares you the dense academic jargon behind this realization and incorporates it into practical routines you can implement simply and easily into your daily routine.

3. IT'S A JOURNAL FOR PEOPLE WHO DON'T WRITE JOURNALS.

If you are the kind of person who always wanted to write a journal, but life, excuses, and email took precedence, look no further. The Five Minute Journal was designed for you. Whatever your excuses are for not keeping a journal, this journal will eliminate them.

4. IT'S A SNAPSHOT OF YOUR POSITIVE EXPERIENCES.

Think of the feeling that arises when you smile nostalgically at an old photo of yourself. Imagine if you could have the same experience by just flipping to a certain day on a specific year in your life: you could zoom in on who you were, what you did, and how you felt on that day. It will be your own chronicle of memories, ideas, and dreams.

5. IT'S A COMMITMENT YOU CAN STICK TO.

Inside you will find ways to foolproof your commitment to writing frequently. How often do we shrink away from practices that we know are good for us? Unhealthy doctors, procrastinating professors, and unfaithful presidents prove this point. Simple and effective actions will get you in the habit of journaling every day and focusing on positive changes in your life.

We are what we repeatedly do. Excellence, then, is not an act, *but a habit*.

WILL DURANT

How it Works

It is likely you have come across quotes like the one from Durant on the left. They make us evaluate our present habits in a split second and think about the things we need to change. Even if you consider yourself to be ambitious, chances are you find it difficult to implement a series of new behaviors in your life.

You see, common sense is hardly common action.

That is why 44% of doctors are overweight[1] despite having spent the majority of their youth buried in books telling them about the merits of exercise and diet. Repeat after us—reading a book on how to ride a bicycle does not qualify you for the Tour de France.

Research in self-control and self-regulation shows willpower to be a limited resource similar to a muscle that tires with use.[2] Chronically stressed humans find it difficult to resist temptation, ranging from the seemingly benign like a latte, to a no-holds-barred shopping spree. What is one to do? Forgo the shopping spree and opt for the latte? Or is there another option?

Fortunately, with a little inspiration from high achievers we have read about, we offer you this neat, little journal. Don't let the simplicity fool you. It combines several principles that can weave the fabric of your new life.

Basic Principles

Wisdom from ancient and modern times teaches us that the beginning and the end of the day are times to think, evaluate, and correct course. Regardless of when your day begins or ends, few people have established positive rituals that allow them to thrive.

Contrary to popular opinion, such established positive rituals are not restricted to the domain of ultra-successful CEOs or Buddhist monks.

We recommend you keep this journal with a pen at your bedside. Let this be the first impulse when you wake up and the final impulse before you sleep. Let The Five Minute Journal hold that coveted spot on your bedside table, just an arm's reach away. You will be richly rewarded.

In about five minutes per day, you can establish a positive pattern of thinking and acting when it really matters. It's the ideal time window that allows for minimal effort and a wild reward.

Onward.

Early to bed, early to rise, makes a man healthy, wealthy *and wise*.

BENJAMIN FRANKLIN

WHY SHOULD I WRITE AS SOON
AS I WAKE UP?

Have you ever had a day when you woke up and it felt like everything was going your way? Things just felt easy, even effortless, and you couldn't help but smile? Is there a way that you can get a taste of that every day?

The Five Minute Journal is designed to help you do just that. You are fresh, still waking up and have the precious opportunity in the first few minutes to set the tone for the rest of the day. The journal asks you the precise questions that will create positive habit loops.

Make sure to write the journal first thing in the morning, even if you are:

Still sleepy? Thanks for sharing. Write it anyway.

Feeling unmotivated? Thanks for sharing. Write it anyway.

Late for work? Thanks for sharing. Write it anyway.

Growth isn't all roses and honey. It isn't always comfortable and it doesn't come with a cute bow tied over it.

The reward of growth is priceless. Growth can lead to fulfilling relationships, improved health, and a good night's sleep.

Resistance can get in the way of the growth you need. It causes depression, weakness, and credit card debt.

When you write the journal every morning, you push past resistance. You give yourself the opportunity to grow. You make the commitment to keep going, to make your mark on the world.

Never go to sleep without a request to your *subconscious.*

THOMAS EDISON

What do you typically do before you go to sleep? Do you have a routine?

The average American watches 5 hours and 11 minutes of TV per day.[3] If TV isn't as popular by the time you read this, then you are most likely on your phone or a new electronic device. Much of this happens just before sleep. What if you chose to use this time to invest in yourself? In your well-being?

Writing the journal before you go to sleep is a step in the right direction. Let it be one habit that you do every day (we also recommend brushing and flossing your teeth).

Spectacular results are a product of intelligent design and herculean consistency. Take the example of maintaining harmony in relationships. Some people's relationships have more drama than a reality TV show. Yet, there are others who continue to deepen their love and hardly fight.

There is a little known secret that is shared by couples in fulfilling relationships. It makes them happier and creates lasting bonds.

Here's the secret: They resolve any conflict before they go to sleep—with love, honesty, and trust.

In the same way, it is important that you write the journal before you go to sleep. You will find that The Five Minute Journal instantly helps you shift your focus on the positive and short-circuits negative thought loops. No matter how your day was, you will sleep a bit better than you would have otherwise. Simple.

Make sure to write the journal before going to sleep. Even if you:

Had a long day? Thanks for sharing. Write it anyway.

Have a pounding headache? Thanks for sharing. Write it anyway.

Have an early morning tomorrow? Thanks for sharing. Write it anyway.

The Morning Routine

Today's Gratitude List

One of the greatest strengths we possess as humans is our ability to focus our minds on whatever we choose. If you are perfectly calm and still on the inside, you can handle anything. For those of us without Zen training, the best way you can begin your day is by counting your blessings.

It is the antithesis of a bad-hair day or waking up on the wrong side of the bed. We suggest that whichever side of the bed you have put this journal, it is the right side.

No matter where you are and what your situation is, your focus can be shifted to something positive. Here is how it looks in practice:

I am grateful for…

1. The warm bed that I sleep in.
2. My body that is working in perfect harmony.
3. The true and genuine friends in my life.

OUR SECRET TO THE GRATITUDE LIST

Try writing things you are grateful for that you may not yet have in your life. Let's say you really want to be in a healthy relationship. Then write… *I am grateful to be in a loving, healthy relationship with a partner of my dreams.* Just do not forget to clearly define this person, which is a whole different exercise.

What is Gratitude?

It is an emotion that defies easy classification. Gratitude, derived from the Latin word *gratia* (meaning grace, graciousness or gratefulness) eludes simple explanation by academics. Definitions such as "the willingness to recognize the unearned increments of value in one's experience" look great on term papers but don't get the point across. We will not attempt to disguise imprecision with ten-dollar words.

Gratitude is the experience of counting one's blessings.

It is the feeling that embodies the phrase "Thank you". It is the unexpected reward of a kind deed that is magically produced by your brain. It is the inexplicable feeling in your body that makes you smile at strangers.

Why do scientists love gratitude? Even after cutting through the smoke of Law of Attraction-style belief systems, gratitude has shown to be quite transformative in humans ranging from students to retirees.

A 2003 study by Emmons and McCullough found that keeping a daily gratitude journal leads to better sleep, reductions of physical pain, a greater sense of well-being, and a better ability to handle change.[4]

Delving deeper into the world of brain science, there's another study that illustrates the immediate effectiveness of gratitude. Turns out, gratitude could be the ultimate magic pill for "happiness" (drugs notwithstanding).

In a 2008 study, subjects experiencing gratitude were studied under fMRI (functional Magnetic Resonance Imaging) and it was found that they were influencing their hypothalamus in real-time.[5]

The hypothalamus is the small but powerful part of your brain that directly influences sleep, eating, and stress. Gratitude also stimulates the part of the brain associated with the neurotransmitter dopamine—the "do it again" chemical—that is responsible for the creation of new learning pathways.

Bottom line: writing in this journal each morning and night can help you gain a more positive outlook on life.

Creating
a Better Day

WHAT WOULD MAKE TODAY GREAT?

Have you ever had the experience of buying a new car and seeing the same model everywhere you go?

Or automatically noticing how someone has the same shoes/haircut/shirt? Have you had the experience of falling in love and seeing the world through rose-colored glasses?

These experiences are universal, but why do they happen?

There is a small part of your brain called the Reticular Activation System (RAS) that turns on and off your perception of ideas and thoughts and determines the lenses through which you look at the world. When you take an action like buying a new car, you have taken a major step in redefining your possessions and your RAS changes to accommodate your new acquisition. Everywhere you go, your RAS will gently remind you of this change by pointing out others who have the same car as you.

When you write "What would make today great?" you are taking a step to influence your RAS to point out and engage in activities that would make your day better. You are building new pathways in your brain that allow you to "see" what you can do to improve your well-being every day.

You are creating a new program in your mind that naturally increases your happiness. Doing this consistently gives you consistently better days. It is that simple.

One study found that people who simply thought about watching their favorite funny movie actually increased their endorphin levels (the chemical your brain produces to make you feel happiness and well-being) by 27 percent.[6] The most enjoyable part of an activity is often the anticipation.

To illustrate this with an example, let's introduce you to Katie. She is an ambitious twenty-something whose favorite part of The Five Minute Journal is "What would make today great?" because it gives her an excuse to brainstorm ideas to spice up her day. As soon as she wakes up, she spends an extra minute before writing out this section.

This is what a random day in her journal looks like:

What would make today great?

1. *Being able to take extra time for myself before leaving for work.*
2. *The love my Mom shows me; I will write her a thank you note.*
3. *Getting to sleep before 10 PM.*

Notice she makes sure she writes down what she has control over. She could write about being grateful for a sunny day; however, she has no control over whether the day would be sunny or not. She focuses on the specific actions she can take in the day to make it great.
So, it's your turn now. How could you make today great for you?

It's the *repetition of affirmations* that leads to belief. And once that belief becomes a deep conviction, things begin to happen.

MUHAMMAD ALI

Daily Affirmation

If you have read this far, chances are you are interested in creating something amazing in your life and you are going to achieve it. You have ideas about the person you want to be and the future you want to build.

Let's consider a study conducted by Dr. Alia Crum and Dr. Ellen Langer from Harvard University. They performed an experiment to study the effect of brain priming on the staff of seven different hotels. Half of the participants were informed about how much exercise they were getting every day through their work—how many calories they burned, how similar vacuuming is to a workout, etc. The other half were given no such information.

Several weeks later, it was found that the first group who had been primed to think of their work as exercise had actually lost weight. Incredibly, these individuals had not done any more work or exercised any more than the control group (their colleagues who had not been informed about how their work was similar to a workout).[7]

Hence the operative question—how can you prime your brain to cash in on this?

The Daily Affirmation is a simple statement that defines you as you want to be. Every time you write the daily affirmation, you prime your brain to start building this belief in your mind. With consistency, you will begin to create that change from within.

HERE IS HOW IT WORKS IN PRACTICE.

Let's say Bruce is interested in building his confidence in everyday life. He wakes up in the morning and writes in his journal:

Daily affirmation

I am confident and comfortable in my own skin.

As he goes about his day, he naturally starts to notice the world from this perspective. Let's say he buys some tea and smiles at the cashier. His subconscious begins to think, "Ah, this must be happening because I am confident and comfortable in my own skin." Every day he writes in The Five Minute Journal, he begins to prime his brain to this belief.

Don't underestimate the effectiveness of this exercise. If Will Smith, Jim Carrey, and Arnold Schwarzenegger found value in it, you can too.

**HERE ARE SOME EXAMPLES OF HOW THIS LOOKS
IN THE JOURNAL:**

Daily affirmation

I am able to live with passion and purpose.

YOU COULD ALSO GET NICE AND SPECIFIC:

Daily affirmation

I am in a loving and passionate relationship.

Earning $100,000 per year.

The Night
Routine

Highlights of the Day

Possibly the best moment in the day is allowing yourself to take inventory of special moments—big and small. Highlights of the Day is your personal collection of the expected and unexpected bounty of good things that you experienced in a day.

To illustrate the effectiveness of this one section, we turn to Quora—a social networking website that allows intelligent people around the world to share insights, answers, and knowledge. A question relating to happiness gleaned a powerful response from a social marketer, Brad Einarsen, which was supported by leading psychologists such as BJ Fogg.

“

BRAD EINARSEN

When I was in a dark period, I instituted a simple rule that changed my life.

Rule:
When I arrive home from work, the very first thing I tell my wife is the best thing that happened that day.

No exceptions. No complaining. Just the best thing that day, even if it was just a good cup of coffee. This had the effect of starting our evening off on a positive note and it changed our relationship.

”

THE HIGHLIGHTS OF THE DAY IN ACTION

To investigate the power of focussing on three good things every day, a group of ICU (Intensive Care Unit) staff were invited to participate in a 14-day study. During the study, the ICU personnel, a group who typically have a higher level of job-related burn-out and post-traumatic stress disorder, were asked to reflect on the questions: "What are the three things that went well today?" and "What was your role in bringing them about?". Researchers identified 3 main themes—having a good day at work; having supportive relationships; and making meaningful use of leisure time—and concluded that focusing on three good things each day not only promoted wellbeing, but also helped to strengthen resilience among the healthcare workers.

FOR THE FIRST FEW WEEKS OF LISTING YOUR HIGHLIGHTS OF THE DAY, START WITH SOMETHING SIMPLE:

Highlights of the Day

1. *A friend recommended a wonderful book for me.*
2. *I took a beautiful walk in the park today.*
3. *Barista remembered how I like my Americano.*

It can truly change your perspective and life outlook. When you write down highlights of the day, you count your blessings—in reverse. This has the effect of allowing you to "prime" your brain in reverse and can change not just your relationships with your loved ones, but your relationship with yourself.

Slowly, you will start to improve at this. Through the power of discipline, the list will start getting better and better. Remember to review Highlights of the Day every month to see how you are changing by focusing on the good in life.

Acknowledging Lessons of Every Day

BECOME BETTER BY DIVING INTO LESSONS LEARNED
AND KNOWLEDGE GAINED FROM EVERY DAY.

Most of our days blend into one another, yet continuous and consistent reflection gives us an opportunity to find out that there is always something different, valuable and insightful in every day. It also encourages us to think about how we can cultivate more intention, joy and meaning in our life.

Finding lessons from every day may be just one of the secrets to your success and emotional well-being, because acknowledging daily life lessons, challenges, and setbacks without letting them define who you are is a great act of courage, self-awareness and mindfulness.

How it works: Review, evaluate and reflect on every aspect of your day. Take a look at your emotional state, at your work and your relationships. What went right? What can be improved?

Helpful hint: Use your everyday experience as a valuable learning tool to become better, grow and unleash your full potential. This is how the growth mindset is built.

It could be finding inspiration in the success of others.
It could be starting your day in control by waking up earlier.
It could be feeling more present when you turn off your phone.

This section is your daily reminder to take full responsibility of your life and shape your own reality. Letting go of what holds you back and turning it into valuable lesson sets you on the path for a more fulfilling tomorrow. It helps you navigate through the challenging times, recognise the good in every day, and live with the intention and purpose.

Let's say today Robin is feeling anxious and stressed because of a very busy schedule at work. She feels like spending some quality time with her loved ones may help her wind down and relax. She decides to log off from work at 7 PM. When she writes in this section, Robin realises she was able to feel calmer and more present at family dinner because she listened to herself, prioritised her wellbeing, and committed to finish her work on time.

SHE WRITES:

What did I learn today?

Always listen to your body - it knows when you need to relax.

And she begins to start building a pattern where she reflects on every day and discovers valuable lessons in her daily choices and actions. In time, this exercise can shift how you react to what every new day brings and help you use your experience as a powerful method for growth and positive change.

HERE ARE MORE EXAMPLES:

What did I learn today?

Reading before the workday starts puts me in a better mood.

Drinking mint tea in the evening helps me fall asleep with ease.

MOST PEOPLE FIND THEMSELVES SMILING WHEN THEY ARE WRITING THIS (HINT, HINT).

The ultimate measure of a man is not where he stands in moments of *comfort and convenience*, but where he stands at times of *challenge and controversy*.

Weekly Challenges

WHERE REAL GROWTH HAPPENS

The weekly challenges will encourage you to take actions beyond your comfort zone, where real growth happens. They are given on a random day of the week instead of the daily quote.

A few thousand years ago, our ancestors dealt with challenges both dangerous and diverse: from staying warm in sub-zero temperatures to fighting other tribes and animals for basic survival. This was the paleolithic human, designed by nature to be incredibly adaptable; they thrived through thick and thin, amidst wars, famine, and ice ages.

Fast forward a few thousand years and the defining challenge of twenty-somethings in our era seems to be getting to Level 3 in the latest mobile-phone game. Progress indeed.

The weekly challenges provided in this book will help you to discover your fears and treat them as allies in your development in life. Treat each challenge as a mission and experiment in your life. You might just enjoy yourself in the process.

My
Commitment

I, _____ *Chloe Moore* _____,

commit to writing The Five Minute Journal for at least 5 days in a row,

starting _____ *May 1* _____.

Writing this journal is really important to me because

I am committing to my best life.

I want to create more abundance in my life.

I need more discipline in my life.

If I finish 5 days of writing this journal, I will reward myself with

A ski trip with my significant other.

If I don't finish 5 days of writing this journal, I will promise to

Donate $100 to a charity I don't support.

I will do the following things to ensure that I do

The Five Minute Journal every day:

Keep my Five Minute Journal right by the bedside.

Brush my teeth only after I've done the journal.

Set my alarm only after I do my night journal.

Share my commitment with someone I love.

Sign up for tips at www.journalhabit.com.

FILL IN THE BLANKS

I, _____,

commit to writing The Five Minute Journal for at least 5 days in a row,

starting _____.

Writing this journal is really important to me because

_____

_____

_____

If I finish 5 days of writing this journal, I will reward myself with

_____

If I don't finish 5 days of writing this journal, I will promise to

_____

I will do the following things to ensure that I do
The Five Minute Journal every day:

_____

_____

_____

_____

_____

_____

The Sticky Solution

Improvement isn't inevitable. Change is.

UNKNOWN

Congratulations! You have just committed to five consecutive days of sticking with this journal. It is a commonly held notion that if you push through resistance and take specific action for a number of days in a row, it becomes an established habit. To give you a head start and ensure that you are sticking with it, here is a healthy push to help you make sure this habit sticks:

The Bad News: Research in 2010 has showed that 88% of people who make New Year's Resolutions fail to keep them.[8]

The Good News: You are better than that. You have already taken more steps than most to ensure you are on the right track.

The Better News: You will be getting tips and tricks to bullet-proof your commitment in the following pages.

TRUTH & ACTIONS
How do I know I'm better today
compared to three years ago?

You don't, unless you are keeping track. It's all too common to assume that we're clearer, more mature, smarter and wiser in our forties than in our teens. An ignorant twenty-something is likely to end up a spectacularly ignorant eighty-something. Conversely, an intelligent teenager intent on seeking wisdom might reliably end up as a wise, oracular sixty-something. The difference? Read on.

SCARY TRUTH NUMBER 1
Minuscule activities lead to massive
improvements (and setbacks).

That job fair gets you your dream job. A new friend devoted to fitness inspires you to train regularly, getting you in the best shape of your life. Starting your mornings off on the right foot leads to the most productive days you have ever had. That is the objective of the journal you are holding.

Alas, all changes are not positive. That traffic jam to the interview crushes your dream job opportunity. An irate family member keeps you up at night, replaying nightmarish scenarios of what you should have said or done.

Fortunately, the universe isn't all chaos. Through it all, there are always patterns, guiding lines, and natural rhythms that yearn to be discovered by the penetrating mind. This is liberating.

SCARY TRUTH NUMBER 2
If you're not moving forward, you're most likely moving
backwards. There is no standing still in life.

Unless you methodically track and do a complete analysis of your day, figuring out what is effective and what is not, your daily activities are not much different from a cow's unconscious grazing on the field. There is no clear purpose, no guiding light that strings your actions together—they are steeped in unconsciousness.

Grow through reflection.

LIBERATING TRUTH NUMBER 3

The right action is the universal problem solver.

Sit down with a cup of your favorite beverage. Proceed to reflect on the following questions:

WHAT IS YOUR BIGGEST CHALLENGE?

This can be anything from creating a better relationship to feeling comfortable in your own skin to becoming more financially stable. Chances are there is something that is on your mind most of the time.

Put it on paper.

_____

_____

_____

WHAT IS ONE IDENTITY STATEMENT THAT WOULD CHANGE EVERYTHING FOR YOU?

Create an identity statement that remedies the above challenge. Every challenge has a remedy. Use this statement in your journal. Stick with this statement until it becomes true in your life. Read the preceding statement again. Engrave it in your mind before moving ahead.

EXAMPLES

I am giving and receiving of profound love and respect.

I am always surrounding myself with people who have a positive influence in my personal growth journey.

I am taking time to practice self love to promote a positive relationship with my body, emotionally, mentally and physically.

Your Identity Statement

Write your identity statement.

_____

_____

_____

_____

_____

What are three major obstacles that would stop you from writing the journal (morning/night)?

1. _____

2. _____

3. _____

Write two actions you can take per obstacle to ensure that your resistance doesn't overpower your will.

1. _____

_____

2. _____

_____

3. _____

_____

The key to growth is to learn to make promises and to *keep them.*

STEPHEN R. COVEY

Accountability

Choose a way to keep yourself accountable for writing the journal.

Immerse yourself in tips, videos, and reminders by signing up to receive our curated series of emails designed specifically for The Five Minute Journal owners like you. Go to journalhabit.com to sign up.

Pick a close friend or significant other you can rely on to check on you daily through text—similar to an AA Sponsor. This can also work well if you have received this as a gift from a friend.

If you are more comfortable using pen and paper, just check off every day that you finish the journal in a calendar. There is nothing like a powerful visual reminder of commitment. You can use apps like coach.me or stickk.com to stay accountable.

Choose your method of accountability, and let's begin!

The
Journal

Gratitude unlocks the fullness of life. It turns what we have into enough, and more. It turns denial into acceptance, chaos to order, confusion to clarity.

MELODY BEATTIE

I am grateful for...

1. The warm bed that I sleep in.
2. My body that is working in perfect harmony.
3. The incredible friends in my life.

What would make today great?

1. Taking extra time for myself before leaving work.
2. Giving a thank you note to Mom.
3. Sleeping before 10 PM.

Daily affirmation

I am confident and comfortable in my own skin.

I am living with passion and purpose.

Highlights of the Day

1. I remembered to call my friend and we had a good chat.
2. A colleague recommended a wonderful book for me.
3. I saw a cute stranger at the cafe and sayed "Hi".

What did I learn today?

Communicating openly with my boss helps me avoid stress.

Working out in the morning makes me energized and happy.

37

When life is sweet, say "thank you" and celebrate.
And when life is bitter, say "thank you" and grow.

SHAUNA NIEQUIST

I am grateful for...

1. _____
2. _____
3. _____

What would make today great?

1. _____
2. _____
3. _____

Daily affirmation

_____
_____

Highlights of the Day

1. _____
2. _____
3. _____

What did I learn today?

_____
_____

Very little is needed to make a happy life;
it's all within yourself, in your way of thinking.

MARCUS AURELIUS

I am grateful for...

1. _____
2. _____
3. _____

What would make today great?

1. _____
2. _____
3. _____

Daily affirmation

_____

_____

Highlights of the Day

1. _____
2. _____
3. _____

What did I learn today?

_____

_____

WEEKLY CHALLENGE
Write a text, email, or letter of gratitude to someone you truly care about.

I am grateful for...

1. _____
2. _____
3. _____

What would make today great?

1. _____
2. _____
3. _____

Daily affirmation

_____
_____

Highlights of the Day

1. _____
2. _____
3. _____

What did I learn today?

_____
_____

*What we do every day matters more than what we do
once in a while.*

GRETCHEN RUBIN

I am grateful for...

1. _____

2. _____

3. _____

What would make today great?

1. _____

2. _____

3. _____

Daily affirmation

_____

_____

Highlights of the Day

1. _____

2. _____

3. _____

What did I learn today?

_____

_____

Life is an echo. What you send out comes back.
What you sow you reap. What you give you get.
What you see in others exists in you.

ZIG ZIGLAR

I am grateful for...

1. _____
2. _____
3. _____

What would make today great?

1. _____
2. _____
3. _____

Daily affirmation

_____

_____

Highlights of the Day

1. _____
2. _____
3. _____

What did I learn today?

_____

_____

My Commitment Review

Congratulations on reaching day 5! How was it for you? Take a few moments to reflect on how you've used The Five Minute Journal and how this has made you feel. Have you fulfilled your commitment to writing in the journal every morning and evening? Are you able to focus on the highlights of each day? Have you attended to your daily gratitudes and affirmations?

Think back to the commitment you made to yourself on page 29. How do you feel reading through your entries now? Remember that committing to this journal is the simplest, most effective thing you can do every day to be happier. And don't forget to reward yourself! Make sure to block out time in your schedule to follow this through and enjoy your reward—you've earned it.

Now that you've completed your first 5 days, you can confidently move forward with the The Five Minute Journal at your side. Here at Intelligent Change we know that community support is important to keep us on track, and that's why we have a wealth of resources and inspiration ready for you.

Head over to our Instagram page
@INTELLIGENTCHANGE *to join us.*

Who looks outside, dreams. Who looks inside, awakes.

CARL JUNG

I am grateful for...

1. _____
2. _____
3. _____

What would make today great?

1. _____
2. _____
3. _____

Daily affirmation

_____

_____

Highlights of the Day

1. _____
2. _____
3. _____

What did I learn today?

_____

_____

Surround yourself with people that inspire you and you will not only grow—you will soar.

MIMI IKONN

I am grateful for...

1. _____

2. _____

3. _____

What would make today great?

1. _____

2. _____

3. _____

Daily affirmation

_____

_____

Highlights of the Day

1. _____

2. _____

3. _____

What did I learn today?

_____

_____

45

Each day is a different one, each day brings a miracle of its own.
It's just a matter of paying attention to this miracle.
PAULO COELHO

I am grateful for...

1. _____
2. _____
3. _____

What would make today great?

1. _____
2. _____
3. _____

Daily affirmation

_____

_____

Highlights of the Day

1. _____
2. _____
3. _____

What did I learn today?

_____

_____

*Wake up early, enjoy peaceful morning hours, and greet
a new day by watching the sunrise.*

I am grateful for...

1. _____
2. _____
3. _____

What would make today great?

1. _____
2. _____
3. _____

Daily affirmation

_____

_____

Highlights of the Day

1. _____
2. _____
3. _____

What did I learn today?

_____

_____

A fit body, a calm mind, a house full of love.
These things cannot be bought – they must be earned.
NAVAL RAVIKANT

I am grateful for...

1. _____
2. _____
3. _____

What would make today great?

1. _____
2. _____
3. _____

Daily affirmation

_____
_____

Highlights of the Day

1. _____
2. _____
3. _____

What did I learn today?

_____
_____

*I've found that there is always some beauty left—
in nature, sunshine, freedom, in yourself;
these can all help you.*

ANNE FRANK

I am grateful for...

1. _____
2. _____
3. _____

What would make today great?

1. _____
2. _____
3. _____

Daily affirmation

_____

_____

Highlights of the Day

1. _____
2. _____
3. _____

What did I learn today?

_____

_____

We need to do a better job of putting ourselves higher on our own to-do list.

MICHELLE OBAMA

I am grateful for...

1. _____
2. _____
3. _____

What would make today great?

1. _____
2. _____
3. _____

Daily affirmation

_____

_____

Highlights of the Day

1. _____
2. _____
3. _____

What did I learn today?

_____

_____

You cannot be lonely if you like the person
you are alone with.
WAYNE DYER

I am grateful for...

1. _____
2. _____
3. _____

What would make today great?

1. _____
2. _____
3. _____

Daily affirmation

_____

_____

Highlights of the Day

1. _____
2. _____
3. _____

What did I learn today?

_____

_____

WEEKLY CHALLENGE
Take a break from social media today and be present with your thoughts.

I am grateful for...

1. _____
2. _____
3. _____

What would make today great?

1. _____
2. _____
3. _____

Daily affirmation

_____
_____

Highlights of the Day

1. _____
2. _____
3. _____

What did I learn today?

_____
_____

Nothing new can come into your life unless you are grateful for what you already have.

MICHAEL BERNARD

I am grateful for...

1. _____
2. _____
3. _____

What would make today great?

1. _____
2. _____
3. _____

Daily affirmation

_____

_____

Highlights of the Day

1. _____
2. _____
3. _____

What did I learn today?

_____

_____

Accept no one's definition of your life; define yourself.
HARVEY FIERSTEIN

I am grateful for...

1. _____
2. _____
3. _____

What would make today great?

1. _____
2. _____
3. _____

Daily affirmation

_____

_____

Highlights of the Day

1. _____
2. _____
3. _____

What did I learn today?

_____

_____

Change will not come if we wait for some other person or some other time. We are the ones we've been waiting for. We are the change that we seek.

BARACK OBAMA

I am grateful for...

1. _____
2. _____
3. _____

What would make today great?

1. _____
2. _____
3. _____

Daily affirmation

_____

_____

Highlights of the Day

1. _____
2. _____
3. _____

What did I learn today?

_____

_____

*Happiness is an inside job. Don't assign anyone else
that much power over your life.*

MANDY HALE

I am grateful for...

1. _____
2. _____
3. _____

What would make today great?

1. _____
2. _____
3. _____

Daily affirmation

_____

_____

Highlights of the Day

1. _____
2. _____
3. _____

What did I learn today?

_____

_____

*Life is a journey, and if you fall in love with the journey,
you will be in love forever.*

PETER HAGERTY

I am grateful for...

1. _____
2. _____
3. _____

What would make today great?

1. _____
2. _____
3. _____

Daily affirmation

_____

_____

Highlights of the Day

1. _____
2. _____
3. _____

What did I learn today?

_____

_____

WEEKLY CHALLENGE

The gift of learning to meditate is the greatest gift you can give yourself in this lifetime. Try meditating today for 5 minutes. Just be present with your breath.

I am grateful for...

1. _____
2. _____
3. _____

What would make today great?

1. _____
2. _____
3. _____

Daily affirmation

_____
_____

Highlights of the Day

1. _____
2. _____
3. _____

What did I learn today?

_____
_____

Start each day with a grateful heart.
UNKNOWN

I am grateful for...

1. _____
2. _____
3. _____

What would make today great?

1. _____
2. _____
3. _____

Daily affirmation

_____

_____

Highlights of the Day

1. _____
2. _____
3. _____

What did I learn today?

_____

_____

59

*Challenges are what make life interesting and
overcoming them is what makes life meaningful.*
JOSHUA J. MARINE

I am grateful for...

1. _____
2. _____
3. _____

What would make today great?

1. _____
2. _____
3. _____

Daily affirmation

_____

_____

Highlights of the Day

1. _____
2. _____
3. _____

What did I learn today?

_____

_____

Your biggest commitment must always be to yourself.
BRIDGETT DEVOUE

I am grateful for...

1. _____
2. _____
3. _____

What would make today great?

1. _____
2. _____
3. _____

Daily affirmation

_____

_____

Highlights of the Day

1. _____
2. _____
3. _____

What did I learn today?

_____

_____

*You, and only you, are ultimately responsible for
who you become and how happy you are.*
RACHEL HOLLIS

I am grateful for...

1. _____
2. _____
3. _____

What would make today great?

1. _____
2. _____
3. _____

Daily affirmation

_____
_____

Highlights of the Day

1. _____
2. _____
3. _____

What did I learn today?

_____
_____

Magic is believing in yourself. If you can do that,
you can make anything happen.

JOHANN WOLFGANG VON GOETHE

I am grateful for...

1. _____
2. _____
3. _____

What would make today great?

1. _____
2. _____
3. _____

Daily affirmation

_____

_____

Highlights of the Day

1. _____
2. _____
3. _____

What did I learn today?

_____

_____

If you see something beautiful in someone, speak it.
RUTHIE LINDSEY

I am grateful for...

1. _____
2. _____
3. _____

What would make today great?

1. _____
2. _____
3. _____

Daily affirmation

_____
_____

Highlights of the Day

1. _____
2. _____
3. _____

What did I learn today?

_____
_____

One thing that is beautiful about me is _____.
Acknowledge it and celebrate it.

I am grateful for...

1. _____
2. _____
3. _____

What would make today great?

1. _____
2. _____
3. _____

Daily affirmation

_____
_____

Highlights of the Day

1. _____
2. _____
3. _____

What did I learn today?

_____
_____

Happiness is when what you think, what you say,
and what you do are in harmony.

MAHATMA GANDHI

I am grateful for...

1. _____

2. _____

3. _____

What would make today great?

1. _____

2. _____

3. _____

Daily affirmation

_____

_____

Highlights of the Day

1. _____

2. _____

3. _____

What did I learn today?

_____

_____

The art of peaceful living comes down to living compassionately and wisely.

ALLAN LOKOS

I am grateful for...

1. _____
2. _____
3. _____

What would make today great?

1. _____
2. _____
3. _____

Daily affirmation

_____

_____

Highlights of the Day

1. _____
2. _____
3. _____

What did I learn today?

_____

_____

Who you are tomorrow begins with what you do today.
TIM FARGO

I am grateful for...

1. _____
2. _____
3. _____

What would make today great?

1. _____
2. _____
3. _____

Daily affirmation

_____
_____

Highlights of the Day

1. _____
2. _____
3. _____

What did I learn today?

_____
_____

Attention is the most basic form of love. By paying attention we let ourselves be touched by life, and our hearts naturally become more open and engaged.

TARA BRACH

I am grateful for...

1. _____
2. _____
3. _____

What would make today great?

1. _____
2. _____
3. _____

Daily affirmation

_____

_____

Highlights of the Day

1. _____
2. _____
3. _____

What did I learn today?

_____

_____

WEEKLY CHALLENGE
*Leave a positive review on a product or business
that has changed your life for the better.*

I am grateful for...

1. _____
2. _____
3. _____

What would make today great?

1. _____
2. _____
3. _____

Daily affirmation

_____

_____

Highlights of the Day

1. _____
2. _____
3. _____

What did I learn today?

_____

_____

*Go confidently in the direction of your dreams
and live the life you have imagined.*

HENRY DAVID THOREAU

I am grateful for...

1. _____

2. _____

3. _____

What would make today great?

1. _____

2. _____

3. _____

Daily affirmation

_____

_____

Highlights of the Day

1. _____

2. _____

3. _____

What did I learn today?

_____

_____

Put your heart, mind and soul into your smallest acts.
This is the secret of success.
SWAMI SIVANANDA

I am grateful for...

1. _____
2. _____
3. _____

What would make today great?

1. _____
2. _____
3. _____

Daily affirmation

_____

_____

Highlights of the Day

1. _____
2. _____
3. _____

What did I learn today?

_____

_____

72

Don't sit down and wait for the opportunities to come.
Get up and make them.

MADAM C.J. WALKER

I am grateful for...

1. _____
2. _____
3. _____

What would make today great?

1. _____
2. _____
3. _____

Daily affirmation

_____

_____

Highlights of the Day

1. _____
2. _____
3. _____

What did I learn today?

_____

_____

73

Thankfulness may consist merely of words.
Gratitude is shown in acts.

DAVID O. MCKAY

I am grateful for...

1. _____
2. _____
3. _____

What would make today great?

1. _____
2. _____
3. _____

Daily affirmation

_____

_____

Highlights of the Day

1. _____
2. _____
3. _____

What did I learn today?

_____

_____

WEEKLY CHALLENGE
*Take a 10 (or more) minute walk in a peaceful setting today,
be fully present and listen to world around you.*

I am grateful for...

1. _____
2. _____
3. _____

What would make today great?

1. _____
2. _____
3. _____

Daily affirmation

_____
_____

Highlights of the Day

1. _____
2. _____
3. _____

What did I learn today?

_____
_____

If you don't like something, change it.
If you can't change it, change your attitude.
MAYA ANGELOU

I am grateful for...

1. _____
2. _____
3. _____

What would make today great?

1. _____
2. _____
3. _____

Daily affirmation

_____
_____

Highlights of the Day

1. _____
2. _____
3. _____

What did I learn today?

_____
_____

Be as you wish to seem.
SOCRATES

I am grateful for...

1. _____
2. _____
3. _____

What would make today great?

1. _____
2. _____
3. _____

Daily affirmation

_____

_____

Highlights of the Day

1. _____
2. _____
3. _____

What did I learn today?

_____

_____

Don't settle for average. Bring your best to the moment.
ANGELA BASSETT

I am grateful for...

1. _____
2. _____
3. _____

What would make today great?

1. _____
2. _____
3. _____

Daily affirmation

_____

_____

Highlights of the Day

1. _____
2. _____
3. _____

What did I learn today?

_____

_____

Accept responsibility for your life. Know that it is you
who will get you where you want to go, no one else.
LES BROWN

I am grateful for...

1. _____
2. _____
3. _____

What would make today great?

1. _____
2. _____
3. _____

Daily affirmation

_____

_____

Highlights of the Day

1. _____
2. _____
3. _____

What did I learn today?

_____

_____

WEEKLY CHALLENGE

Being nostalgic can boost your happiness. Remember a very special memory of when you were unconditionally happy. Revive that moment to the last detail.

I am grateful for...

1. _____

2. _____

3. _____

What would make today great?

1. _____

2. _____

3. _____

Daily affirmation

_____

_____

Highlights of the Day

1. _____

2. _____

3. _____

What did I learn today?

_____

_____

There is a powerful driving force inside every human being that, once unleashed, can make any vision, dream, or desire a reality.

TONY ROBBINS

I am grateful for...

1. _____
2. _____
3. _____

What would make today great?

1. _____
2. _____
3. _____

Daily affirmation

_____
_____

Highlights of the Day

1. _____
2. _____
3. _____

What did I learn today?

_____
_____

Life is a story we create moment by moment.
ALEX IKONN

I am grateful for...

1. _____
2. _____
3. _____

What would make today great?

1. _____
2. _____
3. _____

Daily affirmation

_____

_____

Highlights of the Day

1. _____
2. _____
3. _____

What did I learn today?

_____

_____

> *Your actions reveal not what you want,*
> *but what you choose.*
>
> **SHANE PARRISH**

I am grateful for...

1. _____
2. _____
3. _____

What would make today great?

1. _____
2. _____
3. _____

Daily affirmation

_____

_____

Highlights of the Day

1. _____
2. _____
3. _____

What did I learn today?

_____

_____

Self-confidence and self-love is not a destination I just arrive at. It's more of a journey.

JESSICA WILLIAMS

I am grateful for...

1. _____
2. _____
3. _____

What would make today great?

1. _____
2. _____
3. _____

Daily affirmation

_____

_____

Highlights of the Day

1. _____
2. _____
3. _____

What did I learn today?

_____

_____

84

You should never do something kind in hopes of recognition.
Do it because it's right. Do it because it makes you feel good.
SCOOTER BRAUN

I am grateful for...

1. _____
2. _____
3. _____

What would make today great?

1. _____
2. _____
3. _____

Daily affirmation

_____
_____

Highlights of the Day

1. _____
2. _____
3. _____

What did I learn today?

_____
_____

Wherever you are—be all there.

JIM ELLIOT

I am grateful for...

1. _____
2. _____
3. _____

What would make today great?

1. _____
2. _____
3. _____

Daily affirmation

_____
_____

Highlights of the Day

1. _____
2. _____
3. _____

What did I learn today?

_____
_____

WEEKLY CHALLENGE

Pause today for an extra few moments with each question to really connect with the feeling behind what you write down.

I am grateful for...

1. _____
2. _____
3. _____

What would make today great?

1. _____
2. _____
3. _____

Daily affirmation

_____

_____

Highlights of the Day

1. _____
2. _____
3. _____

What did I learn today?

_____

_____

There is no way to happiness—happiness is the way.
THICH NHAT HANH

I am grateful for...

1. _____
2. _____
3. _____

What would make today great?

1. _____
2. _____
3. _____

Daily affirmation

_____
_____

Highlights of the Day

1. _____
2. _____
3. _____

What did I learn today?

_____
_____

Never limit yourself because of others' limited imagination;
never limit others because of your own limited imagination.

DR. MAE JEMISON

I am grateful for...

1. _____
2. _____
3. _____

What would make today great?

1. _____
2. _____
3. _____

Daily affirmation

_____

_____

Highlights of the Day

1. _____
2. _____
3. _____

What did I learn today?

_____

_____

A person's success in life can usually be measured by the number of uncomfortable conversations he or she is willing to have.

TIM FERRISS

I am grateful for...

1. _____
2. _____
3. _____

What would make today great?

1. _____
2. _____
3. _____

Daily affirmation

_____
_____

Highlights of the Day

1. _____
2. _____
3. _____

What did I learn today?

_____
_____

You always gain by giving love.
REESE WITHERSPOON

I am grateful for...

1. _____
2. _____
3. _____

What would make today great?

1. _____
2. _____
3. _____

Daily affirmation

_____
_____

Highlights of the Day

1. _____
2. _____
3. _____

What did I learn today?

_____
_____

When we are no longer able to change a situation,
we are challenged to change ourselves.

VIKTOR E. FRANKL

I am grateful for...

1. _____
2. _____
3. _____

What would make today great?

1. _____
2. _____
3. _____

Daily affirmation

_____
_____

Highlights of the Day

1. _____
2. _____
3. _____

What did I learn today?

_____
_____

Mastering others is strength; mastering yourself is true power.
LAO TZU

I am grateful for...

1. _____
2. _____
3. _____

What would make today great?

1. _____
2. _____
3. _____

Daily affirmation

_____
_____

Highlights of the Day

1. _____
2. _____
3. _____

What did I learn today?

_____
_____

WEEKLY CHALLENGE
Spend some time in nature today. Walk barefoot or sit still.

I am grateful for...

1. _____
2. _____
3. _____

What would make today great?

1. _____
2. _____
3. _____

Daily affirmation

_____
_____

Highlights of the Day

1. _____
2. _____
3. _____

What did I learn today?

_____
_____

*Give your gratitude space to grow,
and you will see your whole world change.*
STEVE MARABOLI

I am grateful for...

1. _____
2. _____
3. _____

What would make today great?

1. _____
2. _____
3. _____

Daily affirmation

_____

_____

Highlights of the Day

1. _____
2. _____
3. _____

What did I learn today?

_____

_____

Out of your vulnerabilities will come your strength.
SIGMUND FREUD

I am grateful for...

1. _____
2. _____
3. _____

What would make today great?

1. _____
2. _____
3. _____

Daily affirmation

_____

_____

Highlights of the Day

1. _____
2. _____
3. _____

What did I learn today?

_____

_____

We must discover the power of love, the redemptive power of love. And when we discover that, we will be able to make of this old world a new world. Love is the only way.

MARTIN LUTHER KING JR.

I am grateful for...

1. _____
2. _____
3. _____

What would make today great?

1. _____
2. _____
3. _____

Daily affirmation

_____
_____

Highlights of the Day

1. _____
2. _____
3. _____

What did I learn today?

_____
_____

*Joy is what happens to us when we allow ourselves
to recognize how good things really are.*

MARIANNE WILLIAMSON

I am grateful for...

1. _____

2. _____

3. _____

What would make today great?

1. _____

2. _____

3. _____

Daily affirmation

_____

_____

Highlights of the Day

1. _____

2. _____

3. _____

What did I learn today?

_____

_____

Happiness cannot be traveled to, owned, earned, worn or consumed. Happiness is the spiritual experience of living every minute with love, grace, and gratitude.

DENIS WAITLEY

I am grateful for...

1. _____
2. _____
3. _____

What would make today great?

1. _____
2. _____
3. _____

Daily affirmation

_____

_____

Highlights of the Day

1. _____
2. _____
3. _____

What did I learn today?

_____

_____

WEEKLY CHALLENGE
*Lie on the floor on your back with your eyes closed for
5 minutes (or longer) and just breathe.*

I am grateful for...

1. _____
2. _____
3. _____

What would make today great?

1. _____
2. _____
3. _____

Daily affirmation

_____
_____

Highlights of the Day

1. _____
2. _____
3. _____

What did I learn today?

_____
_____

The best and most beautiful things in the world can't be seen or even touched, they must be felt with the heart.

HELEN KELLER

I am grateful for...

1. _____
2. _____
3. _____

What would make today great?

1. _____
2. _____
3. _____

Daily affirmation

_____

_____

Highlights of the Day

1. _____
2. _____
3. _____

What did I learn today?

_____

_____

To be a star, you must shine your own light.
NAPOLEON HILL

I am grateful for...

1. _____
2. _____
3. _____

What would make today great?

1. _____
2. _____
3. _____

Daily affirmation

_____
_____

Highlights of the Day

1. _____
2. _____
3. _____

What did I learn today?

_____
_____

*When we fulfill our function, which is to truly love
ourselves and share love with others,
then true happiness sets in.*

GABRIELLE BERNSTEIN

I am grateful for...

1. _____

2. _____

3. _____

What would make today great?

1. _____

2. _____

3. _____

Daily affirmation

_____

_____

Highlights of the Day

1. _____

2. _____

3. _____

What did I learn today?

_____

_____

103

*Today is your opportunity to build
the tomorrow you want.*
KEN POIROT

I am grateful for...

1. _____
2. _____
3. _____

What would make today great?

1. _____
2. _____
3. _____

Daily affirmation

_____

_____

Highlights of the Day

1. _____
2. _____
3. _____

What did I learn today?

_____

_____

You have to believe in yourself. That's the secret.
CHARLIE CHAPLIN

I am grateful for...

1. _____
2. _____
3. _____

What would make today great?

1. _____
2. _____
3. _____

Daily affirmation

_____

_____

Highlights of the Day

1. _____
2. _____
3. _____

What did I learn today?

_____

_____

WEEKLY CHALLENGE

Try to be friendly to everyone today. Spend the whole day without complaining, judging or making excuses.
Notice how your mood changes.

I am grateful for...

1. _____
2. _____
3. _____

What would make today great?

1. _____
2. _____
3. _____

Daily affirmation

_____
_____

Highlights of the Day

1. _____
2. _____
3. _____

What did I learn today?

_____
_____

A grateful heart is a beginning of greatness.
JAMES E. FAUST

I am grateful for...

1. _____
2. _____
3. _____

What would make today great?

1. _____
2. _____
3. _____

Daily affirmation

_____
_____

Highlights of the Day

1. _____
2. _____
3. _____

What did I learn today?

_____
_____

You are a living magnet. What you attract into your life
is in harmony with your dominant thoughts.

BRIAN TRACY

I am grateful for...

1. _____
2. _____
3. _____

What would make today great?

1. _____
2. _____
3. _____

Daily affirmation

_____

_____

Highlights of the Day

1. _____
2. _____
3. _____

What did I learn today?

_____

_____

Forever is composed of nows.
EMILY DICKINSON

I am grateful for...

1. _____
2. _____
3. _____

What would make today great?

1. _____
2. _____
3. _____

Daily affirmation

_____

_____

Highlights of the Day

1. _____
2. _____
3. _____

What did I learn today?

_____

_____

109

*I don't have to chase extraordinary moments to find
happiness—it's in front of me if I'm paying attention
and practicing gratitude.*

BRENÉ BROWN

I am grateful for...

1. _____
2. _____
3. _____

What would make today great?

1. _____
2. _____
3. _____

Daily affirmation

_____
_____

Highlights of the Day

1. _____
2. _____
3. _____

What did I learn today?

_____
_____

Song I loved when I was younger is _____.
Listen and dance to it today.

I am grateful for...

1. _____
2. _____
3. _____

What would make today great?

1. _____
2. _____
3. _____

Daily affirmation

_____

_____

Highlights of the Day

1. _____
2. _____
3. _____

What did I learn today?

_____

_____

Happiness depends upon ourselves.
ARISTOTLE

I am grateful for...

1. _____
2. _____
3. _____

What would make today great?

1. _____
2. _____
3. _____

Daily affirmation

_____
_____

Highlights of the Day

1. _____
2. _____
3. _____

What did I learn today?

_____
_____

When we seek to discover the best in others,
we somehow bring out the best in ourselves.

WILLIAM ARTHUR WARD

I am grateful for...

1. _____
2. _____
3. _____

What would make today great?

1. _____
2. _____
3. _____

Daily affirmation

_____

_____

Highlights of the Day

1. _____
2. _____
3. _____

What did I learn today?

_____

_____

*The greatest of human emotions is love. The most valuable of
human gifts is the ability to learn. Therefore learn to love.*

UJ RAMDAS

I am grateful for...

1. _____
2. _____
3. _____

What would make today great?

1. _____
2. _____
3. _____

Daily affirmation

_____
_____

Highlights of the Day

1. _____
2. _____
3. _____

What did I learn today?

_____
_____

The universe buries strange jewels deep within us all,
and then stands back to see if we can find them.

ELIZABETH GILBERT

I am grateful for...

1. _____
2. _____
3. _____

What would make today great?

1. _____
2. _____
3. _____

Daily affirmation

_____
_____

Highlights of the Day

1. _____
2. _____
3. _____

What did I learn today?

_____
_____

*Calmness of mind is one of the beautiful jewels
of wisdom.*

JAMES ALLEN

I am grateful for...

1. _____

2. _____

3. _____

What would make today great?

1. _____

2. _____

3. _____

Daily affirmation

_____

_____

Highlights of the Day

1. _____

2. _____

3. _____

What did I learn today?

_____

_____

*Compliment a cashier, sales assistant, barista or a waitress
and share a kind smile with them.*

I am grateful for...

1. _____
2. _____
3. _____

What would make today great?

1. _____
2. _____
3. _____

Daily affirmation

_____
_____

Highlights of the Day

1. _____
2. _____
3. _____

What did I learn today?

_____
_____

*The happiest people discover their own nature and
match their life to it.*

RAY DALIO

I am grateful for...

1. _____

2. _____

3. _____

What would make today great?

1. _____

2. _____

3. _____

Daily affirmation

_____

_____

Highlights of the Day

1. _____

2. _____

3. _____

What did I learn today?

_____

_____

"Thank you" is the best prayer that anyone could say.
I say that one a lot. Thank you expresses extreme gratitude,
humility, understanding.

ALICE WALKER

I am grateful for...

1. _____
2. _____
3. _____

What would make today great?

1. _____
2. _____
3. _____

Daily affirmation

_____

_____

Highlights of the Day

1. _____
2. _____
3. _____

What did I learn today?

_____

_____

Far too many people are looking for the right person,
instead of trying to be the right person.
GLORIA STEINEM

I am grateful for...

1. _____

2. _____

3. _____

What would make today great?

1. _____

2. _____

3. _____

Daily affirmation

_____

_____

Highlights of the Day

1. _____

2. _____

3. _____

What did I learn today?

_____

_____

Life isn't about finding yourself.
Life is about creating yourself.
GEORGE BERNARD SHAW

I am grateful for...

1. _____
2. _____
3. _____

What would make today great?

1. _____
2. _____
3. _____

Daily affirmation

_____
_____

Highlights of the Day

1. _____
2. _____
3. _____

What did I learn today?

_____
_____

121

Continuous improvement is better than delayed perfection.
MARK TWAIN

I am grateful for...

1. _____
2. _____
3. _____

What would make today great?

1. _____
2. _____
3. _____

Daily affirmation

_____
_____

Highlights of the Day

1. _____
2. _____
3. _____

What did I learn today?

_____
_____

*Dreams are the seeds of change. Nothing ever grows without a
seed, and nothing ever changes without a dream.*

DEBBY BOONE

I am grateful for...

1. _____
2. _____
3. _____

What would make today great?

1. _____
2. _____
3. _____

Daily affirmation

_____
_____

Highlights of the Day

1. _____
2. _____
3. _____

What did I learn today?

_____
_____

123

WEEKLY CHALLENGE
*Make an inspirational collage and hang it where you can
see it or create a mood board on Pinterest.*

I am grateful for...

1. _____
2. _____
3. _____

What would make today great?

1. _____
2. _____
3. _____

Daily affirmation

_____

_____

Highlights of the Day

1. _____
2. _____
3. _____

What did I learn today?

_____

_____

Invent your world. Surround yourself with people, color, sounds, and work that nourish you.

SUSAN ARIEL RAINBOW KENNEDY

I am grateful for...

1. _____
2. _____
3. _____

What would make today great?

1. _____
2. _____
3. _____

Daily affirmation

_____

_____

Highlights of the Day

1. _____
2. _____
3. _____

What did I learn today?

_____

_____

It's not how much we give, but how much love we put into giving.
MOTHER TERESA

I am grateful for...

1. _____
2. _____
3. _____

What would make today great?

1. _____
2. _____
3. _____

Daily affirmation

_____
_____

Highlights of the Day

1. _____
2. _____
3. _____

What did I learn today?

_____
_____

The only way to do great work is to love what you do.
If you haven't found it yet, keep looking. Don't settle.
STEVE JOBS

I am grateful for...

1.
2.
3.

What would make today great?

1.
2.
3.

Daily affirmation

Highlights of the Day

1.
2.
3.

What did I learn today?

127

*Your current life is the result of your previous
choices. If you want something different, begin to
choose differently.*

JOE TICHIO

I am grateful for...

1. _____
2. _____
3. _____

What would make today great?

1. _____
2. _____
3. _____

Daily affirmation

_____
_____

Highlights of the Day

1. _____
2. _____
3. _____

What did I learn today?

_____
_____

*Almost everything will work again if you
unplug it for a few minutes, including you.*
ANNE LAMOTT

I am grateful for...

1. _____
2. _____
3. _____

What would make today great?

1. _____
2. _____
3. _____

Daily affirmation

_____

_____

Highlights of the Day

1. _____
2. _____
3. _____

What did I learn today?

_____

_____

When you view your world with an attitude of gratitude,
you're training yourself to focus on the good in life.

PAUL J. MAYOR

I am grateful for...

1. _____
2. _____
3. _____

What would make today great?

1. _____
2. _____
3. _____

Daily affirmation

_____

_____

Highlights of the Day

1. _____
2. _____
3. _____

What did I learn today?

_____

_____

Someone dear to your heart is _____. Say I love you to them.

I am grateful for...

1. _____
2. _____
3. _____

What would make today great?

1. _____
2. _____
3. _____

Daily affirmation

_____

_____

Highlights of the Day

1. _____
2. _____
3. _____

What did I learn today?

_____

_____

The most beautiful people we have known are those who have known defeat, known suffering, known struggle, known loss, and have found their way out of those depths.

ELISABETH KÜBLER-ROSS

I am grateful for...

1. _____
2. _____
3. _____

What would make today great?

1. _____
2. _____
3. _____

Daily affirmation

_____

_____

Highlights of the Day

1. _____
2. _____
3. _____

What did I learn today?

_____

_____

Nothing in the universe can stop you from letting go and starting over.

GUY FINLEY

I am grateful for...

1. _____
2. _____
3. _____

What would make today great?

1. _____
2. _____
3. _____

Daily affirmation

_____

_____

Highlights of the Day

1. _____
2. _____
3. _____

What did I learn today?

_____

_____

Don't explain your philosophy. Embody it.
EPICTETUS

I am grateful for...

1. _____
2. _____
3. _____

What would make today great?

1. _____
2. _____
3. _____

Daily affirmation

_____
_____

Highlights of the Day

1. _____
2. _____
3. _____

What did I learn today?

_____
_____

Courage doesn't always roar. Sometimes courage is the little voice at the end of the day that says I'll try again tomorrow.

MARY ANNE RADMACHER

I am grateful for...

1. _____
2. _____
3. _____

What would make today great?

1. _____
2. _____
3. _____

Daily affirmation

_____

_____

Highlights of the Day

1. _____
2. _____
3. _____

What did I learn today?

_____

_____

Between stimulus and response there is a space.
In that space is our power to choose our response.
In our response lies our growth and our freedom.

VIKTOR E. FRANKL

I am grateful for...

1. _____
2. _____
3. _____

What would make today great?

1. _____
2. _____
3. _____

Daily affirmation

_____

_____

Highlights of the Day

1. _____
2. _____
3. _____

What did I learn today?

_____

_____

136

Knowing yourself is life's eternal homework.
FELICIA DAY

I am grateful for...

1. _____
2. _____
3. _____

What would make today great?

1. _____
2. _____
3. _____

Daily affirmation

_____
_____

Highlights of the Day

1. _____
2. _____
3. _____

What did I learn today?

_____
_____

WEEKLY CHALLENGE

Bring some fresh air to your space. Rearrange your space, declutter your closet and donate things you no longer need to a charitable organization.

I am grateful for...

1. _____
2. _____
3. _____

What would make today great?

1. _____
2. _____
3. _____

Daily affirmation

_____
_____

Highlights of the Day

1. _____
2. _____
3. _____

What did I learn today?

_____
_____

You demonstrate love by giving it unconditionally to yourself. And as you do, you attract others into your life who are able to love you without conditions.

PAUL FERRINI

I am grateful for...

1. _____
2. _____
3. _____

What would make today great?

1. _____
2. _____
3. _____

Daily affirmation

_____
_____

Highlights of the Day

1. _____
2. _____
3. _____

What did I learn today?

_____
_____

*The measure of achievement is not winning awards.
It's doing something that you appreciate, something you
believe is worthwhile.*

JULIA CHILD

I am grateful for...

1. _____
2. _____
3. _____

What would make today great?

1. _____
2. _____
3. _____

Daily affirmation

_____
_____

Highlights of the Day

1. _____
2. _____
3. _____

What did I learn today?

_____
_____

Gratitude can transform common days into thanksgivings,
turn routine job into joy, and change ordinary opportunities
into blessings.

WILLIAM ARTHUR WARD

I am grateful for...

1. _____
2. _____
3. _____

What would make today great?

1. _____
2. _____
3. _____

Daily affirmation

_____
_____

Highlights of the Day

1. _____
2. _____
3. _____

What did I learn today?

_____
_____

Everyone has oceans to fly, if they have the heart to do it.
Is it reckless? Maybe. But what do dreams know
of boundaries?

AMELIA EARHART

I am grateful for...

1. _____

2. _____

3. _____

What would make today great?

1. _____

2. _____

3. _____

Daily affirmation

_____

_____

Highlights of the Day

1. _____

2. _____

3. _____

What did I learn today?

_____

_____

WEEKLY CHALLENGE

Reflect on where and who you are today. Are you living the life of your dreams? What would you change or improve?
Create an action plan.

I am grateful for...

1. _____
2. _____
3. _____

What would make today great?

1. _____
2. _____
3. _____

Daily affirmation

_____
_____

Highlights of the Day

1. _____
2. _____
3. _____

What did I learn today?

_____
_____

*The secret of happiness: Find something more important
than you are and dedicate your life to it.*

DANIEL C. DENNETT

I am grateful for...

1. _____
2. _____
3. _____

What would make today great?

1. _____
2. _____
3. _____

Daily affirmation

_____

_____

Highlights of the Day

1. _____
2. _____
3. _____

What did I learn today?

_____

_____

When we create peace, harmony and balance in our minds,
we'll find it in our lives.

LOUISE HAY

I am grateful for...

1. _____
2. _____
3. _____

What would make today great?

1. _____
2. _____
3. _____

Daily affirmation

_____
_____

Highlights of the Day

1. _____
2. _____
3. _____

What did I learn today?

_____
_____

145

*Knowing that we can be loved exactly as we are
gives us all the best opportunity for growing into
the healthiest of people.*

FRED ROGERS

I am grateful for...

1. _____
2. _____
3. _____

What would make today great?

1. _____
2. _____
3. _____

Daily affirmation

_____

_____

Highlights of the Day

1. _____
2. _____
3. _____

What did I learn today?

_____

_____

Embrace what you don't know, especially in the beginning, because what you don't know can become your greatest asset.

SARA BLAKELY

I am grateful for...

1. _____

2. _____

3. _____

What would make today great?

1. _____

2. _____

3. _____

Daily affirmation

_____

_____

Highlights of the Day

1. _____

2. _____

3. _____

What did I learn today?

_____

_____

I believe that one of the most important things to learn in life is that you can make a difference in your community no matter who you are or where you live.

ROSALYNN CARTER

I am grateful for...

1. _____
2. _____
3. _____

What would make today great?

1. _____
2. _____
3. _____

Daily affirmation

_____

_____

Highlights of the Day

1. _____
2. _____
3. _____

What did I learn today?

_____

_____

1. Be impeccable with your word.
2. Don't take anything personally. 3. Don't make
assumptions. 4. Always do your best.

DON MIGUEL RUIZ

I am grateful for...

1. _____

2. _____

3. _____

What would make today great?

1. _____

2. _____

3. _____

Daily affirmation

_____

_____

Highlights of the Day

1. _____

2. _____

3. _____

What did I learn today?

_____

_____

149

WEEKLY CHALLENGE
What book makes you feel alive and awaken?
Re-read it and share it with someone special.

I am grateful for...

1. _____

2. _____

3. _____

What would make today great?

1. _____

2. _____

3. _____

Daily affirmation

_____

_____

Highlights of the Day

1. _____

2. _____

3. _____

What did I learn today?

_____

_____

*Everyone of us needs to show how much we care for each other,
and in the process care for ourselves.*

PRINCESS DIANA

I am grateful for...

1. _____

2. _____

3. _____

What would make today great?

1. _____

2. _____

3. _____

Daily affirmation

_____

_____

Highlights of the Day

1. _____

2. _____

3. _____

What did I learn today?

_____

_____

151

Gratitude is one of the most medicinal emotions we can feel.
It elevates our moods and fills us with joy.

SARA AVANT STOVER

I am grateful for...

1. _____
2. _____
3. _____

What would make today great?

1. _____
2. _____
3. _____

Daily affirmation

_____
_____

Highlights of the Day

1. _____
2. _____
3. _____

What did I learn today?

_____
_____

The place to be happy is now.
The time to be happy is now.
ROBERT G. INGERSOLL

I am grateful for...

1. _____
2. _____
3. _____

What would make today great?

1. _____
2. _____
3. _____

Daily affirmation

_____
_____

Highlights of the Day

1. _____
2. _____
3. _____

What did I learn today?

_____
_____

153

There is no elevator to success;
you have to take the stairs.
JULIE RICE

I am grateful for...

1. _____
2. _____
3. _____

What would make today great?

1. _____
2. _____
3. _____

Daily affirmation

_____
_____

Highlights of the Day

1. _____
2. _____
3. _____

What did I learn today?

_____
_____

Mindfulness is about being fully awake in our lives.
JON KABAT-ZINN

I am grateful for...

1. _____
2. _____
3. _____

What would make today great?

1. _____
2. _____
3. _____

Daily affirmation

_____

_____

Highlights of the Day

1. _____
2. _____
3. _____

What did I learn today?

_____

_____

Do not spoil what you have by desiring what you have not;
remember that what you now have was once among the
things you only hoped for.

EPICURUS

I am grateful for...

1. _____

2. _____

3. _____

What would make today great?

1. _____

2. _____

3. _____

Daily affirmation

_____

_____

Highlights of the Day

1. _____

2. _____

3. _____

What did I learn today?

_____

_____

WEEKLY CHALLENGE

Reconnect with an old friend. Send them a message,
give them a call or schedule a (virtual) meeting.

I am grateful for...

1. _____
2. _____
3. _____

What would make today great?

1. _____
2. _____
3. _____

Daily affirmation

_____
_____

Highlights of the Day

1. _____
2. _____
3. _____

What did I learn today?

_____
_____

Love doesn't just sit there, like a stone, it has to be made, like bread; remade all the time, made new.

URSULA LE GUIN

I am grateful for...

1. _____
2. _____
3. _____

What would make today great?

1. _____
2. _____
3. _____

Daily affirmation

_____
_____

Highlights of the Day

1. _____
2. _____
3. _____

What did I learn today?

_____
_____

Life is better when we don't try to do everything. Learn to enjoy the slice of life you experience, and life turns out to be wonderful.
LEO BABAUTA

I am grateful for...

1. _____

2. _____

3. _____

What would make today great?

1. _____

2. _____

3. _____

Daily affirmation

_____

_____

Highlights of the Day

1. _____

2. _____

3. _____

What did I learn today?

_____

_____

You do not find the happy life. You make it.

CAMILLA EYRING KIMBALL

I am grateful for...

1. _____
2. _____
3. _____

What would make today great?

1. _____
2. _____
3. _____

Daily affirmation

_____

_____

Highlights of the Day

1. _____
2. _____
3. _____

What did I learn today?

_____

_____

*Learning is the only thing the mind never exhausts,
never fears, and never regrets.*

LEONARDO DA VINCI

I am grateful for...

1. _____
2. _____
3. _____

What would make today great?

1. _____
2. _____
3. _____

Daily affirmation

_____

_____

Highlights of the Day

1. _____
2. _____
3. _____

What did I learn today?

_____

_____

*We must find time to stop and thank the people
who make a difference in our lives.*

JOHN F. KENNEDY

I am grateful for...

1. _____
2. _____
3. _____

What would make today great?

1. _____
2. _____
3. _____

Daily affirmation

_____

_____

Highlights of the Day

1. _____
2. _____
3. _____

What did I learn today?

_____

_____

It's time to revise your daily routines. What is one special
ritual you wanted to implement into your life?
_____. Start today.

I am grateful for...

1. _____
2. _____
3. _____

What would make today great?

1. _____
2. _____
3. _____

Daily affirmation

_____

_____

Highlights of the Day

1. _____
2. _____
3. _____

What did I learn today?

_____

_____

Trust yourself. Create the kind of self that you will be happy to live with all your life.

GOLDA MEIR

I am grateful for...

1. _____
2. _____
3. _____

What would make today great?

1. _____
2. _____
3. _____

Daily affirmation

_____
_____

Highlights of the Day

1. _____
2. _____
3. _____

What did I learn today?

_____
_____

Anyone who has a why to live can bear almost any what.
FRIEDRICH NIETZSCHE

I am grateful for...

1. _____
2. _____
3. _____

What would make today great?

1. _____
2. _____
3. _____

Daily affirmation

_____

_____

Highlights of the Day

1. _____
2. _____
3. _____

What did I learn today?

_____

_____

We don't need more stuff. We need more humanity.
SETH GODIN

I am grateful for...

1. _____
2. _____
3. _____

What would make today great?

1. _____
2. _____
3. _____

Daily affirmation

_____
_____

Highlights of the Day

1. _____
2. _____
3. _____

What did I learn today?

_____
_____

After everything that's happened,
how can the world still be so beautiful? Because it is.

MARGARET ATWOOD

I am grateful for...

1. _____
2. _____
3. _____

What would make today great?

1. _____
2. _____
3. _____

Daily affirmation

_____
_____

Highlights of the Day

1. _____
2. _____
3. _____

What did I learn today?

_____
_____

167

Mind is a flexible mirror, adjust it to see a better world.
AMIT RAY

I am grateful for...

1. _____
2. _____
3. _____

What would make today great?

1. _____
2. _____
3. _____

Daily affirmation

_____
_____

Highlights of the Day

1. _____
2. _____
3. _____

What did I learn today?

_____
_____

*We have two lives, and the second begins when we realize
we only have one.*

CONFUCIUS

I am grateful for...

1. _____
2. _____
3. _____

What would make today great?

1. _____
2. _____
3. _____

Daily affirmation

_____

_____

Highlights of the Day

1. _____
2. _____
3. _____

What did I learn today?

_____

_____

WEEKLY CHALLENGE
Reflect on what you have achieved recently and celebrate it.

I am grateful for...

1. _____
2. _____
3. _____

What would make today great?

1. _____
2. _____
3. _____

Daily affirmation

_____
_____

Highlights of the Day

1. _____
2. _____
3. _____

What did I learn today?

_____
_____

I am the master of my fate. I am the captain of my soul.
WILLIAM ERNEST HENLEY

I am grateful for...

1. _____
2. _____
3. _____

What would make today great?

1. _____
2. _____
3. _____

Daily affirmation

_____

_____

Highlights of the Day

1. _____
2. _____
3. _____

What did I learn today?

_____

_____

The more I wonder, the more I love.
ALICE WALKER

I am grateful for...

1. _____
2. _____
3. _____

What would make today great?

1. _____
2. _____
3. _____

Daily affirmation

_____
_____

Highlights of the Day

1. _____
2. _____
3. _____

What did I learn today?

_____
_____

172

*The real gift of gratitude is that the more grateful you are,
the more present you become.*

ROBERT HOLDEN

I am grateful for...

1. _____
2. _____
3. _____

What would make today great?

1. _____
2. _____
3. _____

Daily affirmation

_____
_____

Highlights of the Day

1. _____
2. _____
3. _____

What did I learn today?

_____
_____

Remove "shoulds" from your vocabulary this year.
Start your journey of self-love now.
KELLY MARTIN

I am grateful for...

1. _____
2. _____
3. _____

What would make today great?

1. _____
2. _____
3. _____

Daily affirmation

_____
_____

Highlights of the Day

1. _____
2. _____
3. _____

What did I learn today?

_____
_____

You are never too old to reinvent yourself.
STEVE HARVEY

I am grateful for...

1. _____
2. _____
3. _____

What would make today great?

1. _____
2. _____
3. _____

Daily affirmation

_____
_____

Highlights of the Day

1. _____
2. _____
3. _____

What did I learn today?

_____
_____

Be the light that helps others see;
it is what gives life its deepest significance.
ROY T. BENNETT

I am grateful for...

1. _____
2. _____
3. _____

What would make today great?

1. _____
2. _____
3. _____

Daily affirmation

_____

_____

Highlights of the Day

1. _____
2. _____
3. _____

What did I learn today?

_____

_____

WEEKLY CHALLENGE
The funniest movie I've seen is _____.
Lift your spirit and watch it again this week.

I am grateful for...

1. _____
2. _____
3. _____

What would make today great?

1. _____
2. _____
3. _____

Daily affirmation

_____

_____

Highlights of the Day

1. _____
2. _____
3. _____

What did I learn today?

_____

_____

We need, above all things, to slow down.
ALAN WATTS

I am grateful for...

1. _____
2. _____
3. _____

What would make today great?

1. _____
2. _____
3. _____

Daily affirmation

_____
_____

Highlights of the Day

1. _____
2. _____
3. _____

What did I learn today?

_____
_____

If you're not prepared to be wrong,
you'll never come up with anything original.
KEN ROBINSON

I am grateful for...

1. _____
2. _____
3. _____

What would make today great?

1. _____
2. _____
3. _____

Daily affirmation

_____

_____

Highlights of the Day

1. _____
2. _____
3. _____

What did I learn today?

_____

_____

I'm grateful for always this moment, the now,
no matter what form it takes.

ECKHART TOLLE

I am grateful for...

1. _____
2. _____
3. _____

What would make today great?

1. _____
2. _____
3. _____

Daily affirmation

_____

_____

Highlights of the Day

1. _____
2. _____
3. _____

What did I learn today?

_____

_____

*Gratitude is the closest thing to beauty
manifested in an emotion.*

MINDY KALING

I am grateful for...

1. _____
2. _____
3. _____

What would make today great?

1. _____
2. _____
3. _____

Daily affirmation

_____

_____

Highlights of the Day

1. _____
2. _____
3. _____

What did I learn today?

_____

_____

Habits are like financial capital—forming one today is an investment that will automatically give out returns for years to come.

SHAWN ACHOR

I am grateful for...

1. _____
2. _____
3. _____

What would make today great?

1. _____
2. _____
3. _____

Daily affirmation

_____

_____

Highlights of the Day

1. _____
2. _____
3. _____

What did I learn today?

_____

_____

WEEKLY CHALLENGE

Take a different route on your way home or discover a new area.

I am grateful for...

1. _____
2. _____
3. _____

What would make today great?

1. _____
2. _____
3. _____

Daily affirmation

_____
_____

Highlights of the Day

1. _____
2. _____
3. _____

What did I learn today?

_____
_____

Everything you need is already inside.

BILL BOWERMAN

I am grateful for...

1. _____
2. _____
3. _____

What would make today great?

1. _____
2. _____
3. _____

Daily affirmation

_____

_____

Highlights of the Day

1. _____
2. _____
3. _____

What did I learn today?

_____

_____

Appreciation can make a day, even change a life.
Your willingness to put it into words is all that is necessary.
MARGARET COUSINS

I am grateful for...

1. _____
2. _____
3. _____

What would make today great?

1. _____
2. _____
3. _____

Daily affirmation

_____

_____

Highlights of the Day

1. _____
2. _____
3. _____

What did I learn today?

_____

_____

185

Love is not determined by the one being loved
but rather by the one choosing to love.
STEPHEN KENDRICK

I am grateful for...

1. _____
2. _____
3. _____

What would make today great?

1. _____
2. _____
3. _____

Daily affirmation

_____
_____

Highlights of the Day

1. _____
2. _____
3. _____

What did I learn today?

_____
_____

Curiosity is the most powerful thing you own.
Imagination is a force that can actually manifest a reality.
JAMES CAMERON

I am grateful for...

1. _____
2. _____
3. _____

What would make today great?

1. _____
2. _____
3. _____

Daily affirmation

_____
_____

Highlights of the Day

1. _____
2. _____
3. _____

What did I learn today?

_____
_____

*True freedom is understanding that we have a choice
in who and what we allow to have power over us.*

MERYL STREEP

I am grateful for...

1. _____
2. _____
3. _____

What would make today great?

1. _____
2. _____
3. _____

Daily affirmation

_____

_____

Highlights of the Day

1. _____
2. _____
3. _____

What did I learn today?

_____

_____

It's not the mountain that we conquer, but ourselves.
SIR EDMUND HILLARY

I am grateful for...

1. _____
2. _____
3. _____

What would make today great?

1. _____
2. _____
3. _____

Daily affirmation

_____
_____

Highlights of the Day

1. _____
2. _____
3. _____

What did I learn today?

_____
_____

WEEKLY CHALLENGE
*Put your phone in a different room
and read for 30 minutes before going to sleep.*

I am grateful for...

1. _____
2. _____
3. _____

What would make today great?

1. _____
2. _____
3. _____

Daily affirmation

_____
_____

Highlights of the Day

1. _____
2. _____
3. _____

What did I learn today?

_____
_____

If you look hard enough, you will find that even tough times offer pearls worthy of gratitude.

RICHELLE E. GOODRICH

I am grateful for...

1. _____

2. _____

3. _____

What would make today great?

1. _____

2. _____

3. _____

Daily affirmation

_____

_____

Highlights of the Day

1. _____

2. _____

3. _____

What did I learn today?

_____

_____

Strength does not come from winning. Your struggles develop your strengths. When you go through hardships and decide not to surrender, that is strength.

ARNOLD SCHWARZENEGGER

I am grateful for...

1. _____
2. _____
3. _____

What would make today great?

1. _____
2. _____
3. _____

Daily affirmation

_____

_____

Highlights of the Day

1. _____
2. _____
3. _____

What did I learn today?

_____

_____

A smile is a curve that sets everything straight.
PHYLLIS DILLER

I am grateful for...

1. _____
2. _____
3. _____

What would make today great?

1. _____
2. _____
3. _____

Daily affirmation

_____
_____

Highlights of the Day

1. _____
2. _____
3. _____

What did I learn today?

_____
_____

I don't forgive people because I'm weak, I forgive them
because I am strong enough to know people make mistakes.
MARILYN MONROE

I am grateful for...

1. _____
2. _____
3. _____

What would make today great?

1. _____
2. _____
3. _____

Daily affirmation

_____

_____

Highlights of the Day

1. _____
2. _____
3. _____

What did I learn today?

_____

_____

There is no passion to be found playing small—in settling for a life that is less than the one you are capable of living.

NELSON MANDELA

I am grateful for...

1. _____
2. _____
3. _____

What would make today great?

1. _____
2. _____
3. _____

Daily affirmation

_____
_____

Highlights of the Day

1. _____
2. _____
3. _____

What did I learn today?

_____
_____

WEEKLY CHALLENGE
One item in your wardrobe that boosts your confidence is
_____. *Wear it today.*

I am grateful for...

1. _____
2. _____
3. _____

What would make today great?

1. _____
2. _____
3. _____

Daily affirmation

_____

_____

Highlights of the Day

1. _____
2. _____
3. _____

What did I learn today?

_____

_____

*90% of success is just showing up. Get there and start working.
You're not going to feel perfect everyday.*

JOE ROGAN

I am grateful for...

1. _____
2. _____
3. _____

What would make today great?

1. _____
2. _____
3. _____

Daily affirmation

_____
_____

Highlights of the Day

1. _____
2. _____
3. _____

What did I learn today?

_____
_____

*If we have the attitude that it's going to be a great day,
it usually is.*

CATHERINE PULSIFIER

I am grateful for...

1. _____

2. _____

3. _____

What would make today great?

1. _____

2. _____

3. _____

Daily affirmation

_____

_____

Highlights of the Day

1. _____

2. _____

3. _____

What did I learn today?

_____

_____

Don't focus on the pain. Focus on the progress.
DWAYNE JOHNSON

I am grateful for...

1. _____
2. _____
3. _____

What would make today great?

1. _____
2. _____
3. _____

Daily affirmation

_____

_____

Highlights of the Day

1. _____
2. _____
3. _____

What did I learn today?

_____

_____

*Wherever there is a human being,
there is an opportunity for a kindness.*
SENECA

I am grateful for...

1. _____
2. _____
3. _____

What would make today great?

1. _____
2. _____
3. _____

Daily affirmation

_____
_____

Highlights of the Day

1. _____
2. _____
3. _____

What did I learn today?

_____
_____

*Nothing contributes so much to tranquilize
the mind as a steady purpose.*
MARY SHELLEY

I am grateful for...

1. _____
2. _____
3. _____

What would make today great?

1. _____
2. _____
3. _____

Daily affirmation

_____
_____

Highlights of the Day

1. _____
2. _____
3. _____

What did I learn today?

_____
_____

When you give joy to other people,
you get more joy in return.
ELEANOR ROOSEVELT

I am grateful for...

1. _____
2. _____
3. _____

What would make today great?

1. _____
2. _____
3. _____

Daily affirmation

_____

_____

Highlights of the Day

1. _____
2. _____
3. _____

What did I learn today?

_____

_____

Respect is how to treat everyone,
not just those you want to impress.
RICHARD BRANSON

I am grateful for...

1. _____
2. _____
3. _____

What would make today great?

1. _____
2. _____
3. _____

Daily affirmation

_____
_____

Highlights of the Day

1. _____
2. _____
3. _____

What did I learn today?

_____
_____

WEEKLY CHALLENGE

Book yourself a self-care activity of your choice this week.
Massage, yoga class, spa, some me-time, or anything that
will make you feel better.

I am grateful for...

1. _____

2. _____

3. _____

What would make today great?

1. _____

2. _____

3. _____

Daily affirmation

_____

_____

Highlights of the Day

1. _____

2. _____

3. _____

What did I learn today?

_____

_____

*The grateful heart isn't developed in a single moment;
it is the result of a thousand choices.*

PETE WILSON

I am grateful for...

1. _____
2. _____
3. _____

What would make today great?

1. _____
2. _____
3. _____

Daily affirmation

_____
_____

Highlights of the Day

1. _____
2. _____
3. _____

What did I learn today?

_____
_____

It's important to take the time out from living and just appreciate what you've got right in front of you.

L.A. FIRE

I am grateful for...

1. _____

2. _____

3. _____

What would make today great?

1. _____

2. _____

3. _____

Daily affirmation

_____

_____

Highlights of the Day

1. _____

2. _____

3. _____

What did I learn today?

_____

_____

Every day may not be good,
but there is something good in every day.
ALICE MORSE EARLE

I am grateful for...

1. _____
2. _____
3. _____

What would make today great?

1. _____
2. _____
3. _____

Daily affirmation

_____

_____

Highlights of the Day

1. _____
2. _____
3. _____

What did I learn today?

_____

_____

207

I feel that the simplicity of life is just being yourself.
BOBBY BROWN

I am grateful for...

1. _____
2. _____
3. _____

What would make today great?

1. _____
2. _____
3. _____

Daily affirmation

_____
_____

Highlights of the Day

1. _____
2. _____
3. _____

What did I learn today?

_____
_____

Take chances, make mistakes. That's how you grow.
Pain nourishes your courage. You have to fail in order to
practice being brave.

MARY TYLER MOORE

I am grateful for...

1. _____
2. _____
3. _____

What would make today great?

1. _____
2. _____
3. _____

Daily affirmation

_____
_____

Highlights of the Day

1. _____
2. _____
3. _____

What did I learn today?

_____
_____

*There are two ways of spreading light: to be the candle,
or the mirror that reflects it.*

EDITH WHARTON

I am grateful for...

1. _____
2. _____
3. _____

What would make today great?

1. _____
2. _____
3. _____

Daily affirmation

_____

_____

Highlights of the Day

1. _____
2. _____
3. _____

What did I learn today?

_____

_____

WEEKLY CHALLENGE

For every hour that you sit today, get up and move for 5–10 minutes. Dance, stretch or go for a quick walk.

I am grateful for...

1. _____
2. _____
3. _____

What would make today great?

1. _____
2. _____
3. _____

Daily affirmation

_____
_____

Highlights of the Day

1. _____
2. _____
3. _____

What did I learn today?

_____
_____

211

Life is strange, beautiful, and terrifying…
and I am thankful for every minute of it that I have had.
I am thankful for every minute yet to come.

BENJAMIN W. BASS

I am grateful for...

1. _____
2. _____
3. _____

What would make today great?

1. _____
2. _____
3. _____

Daily affirmation

_____

_____

Highlights of the Day

1. _____
2. _____
3. _____

What did I learn today?

_____

_____

Action may not always bring happiness;
but there is no happiness without action.
BENJAMIN DISRAELI

I am grateful for...

1. _____
2. _____
3. _____

What would make today great?

1. _____
2. _____
3. _____

Daily affirmation

_____

_____

Highlights of the Day

1. _____
2. _____
3. _____

What did I learn today?

_____

_____

*Life is an unfoldment, and the further we travel
the more truth we can comprehend.*

HYPATIA

I am grateful for...

1. _____

2. _____

3. _____

What would make today great?

1. _____

2. _____

3. _____

Daily affirmation

_____

_____

Highlights of the Day

1. _____

2. _____

3. _____

What did I learn today?

_____

_____

*The less you fear, the more power you'll have
and the more fully you'll live.*
ROBERT GREENE

I am grateful for...

1. _____
2. _____
3. _____

What would make today great?

1. _____
2. _____
3. _____

Daily affirmation

_____

_____

Highlights of the Day

1. _____
2. _____
3. _____

What did I learn today?

_____

_____

*The longer I live, the more I observe that carrying around
anger is the most debilitating to the person who bears it.*

KATHARINE GRAHAM

I am grateful for...

1. _____

2. _____

3. _____

What would make today great?

1. _____

2. _____

3. _____

Daily affirmation

_____

_____

Highlights of the Day

1. _____

2. _____

3. _____

What did I learn today?

_____

_____

One word frees us of all the weight and pain of life.
That word is love.

SOPHOCLES

I am grateful for...

1. _____
2. _____
3. _____

What would make today great?

1. _____
2. _____
3. _____

Daily affirmation

_____

_____

Highlights of the Day

1. _____
2. _____
3. _____

What did I learn today?

_____

_____

217

WEEKLY CHALLENGE
*Pay for someone else's meal or drink this week,
or order a meal for a close family member living far from you.*

I am grateful for...

1. _____
2. _____
3. _____

What would make today great?

1. _____
2. _____
3. _____

Daily affirmation

_____
_____

Highlights of the Day

1. _____
2. _____
3. _____

What did I learn today?

_____
_____

And in the end, it's not the years in your life that count.
It's the life in your years.
EDWARD J. STIEGLITZ

I am grateful for...

1. _____
2. _____
3. _____

What would make today great?

1. _____
2. _____
3. _____

Daily affirmation

_____

_____

Highlights of the Day

1. _____
2. _____
3. _____

What did I learn today?

_____

_____

Life isn't about getting and having,
it's about giving and being.
KEVIN KRUSE

I am grateful for...

1. _____
2. _____
3. _____

What would make today great?

1. _____
2. _____
3. _____

Daily affirmation

_____

_____

Highlights of the Day

1. _____
2. _____
3. _____

What did I learn today?

_____

_____

One of the things I learned the hard way was that it doesn't pay to get discouraged. Keeping busy and making optimism a way of life can restore your faith in yourself.

LUCILLE BALL

I am grateful for...

1. _____

2. _____

3. _____

What would make today great?

1. _____

2. _____

3. _____

Daily affirmation

_____

_____

Highlights of the Day

1. _____

2. _____

3. _____

What did I learn today?

_____

_____

Where there is love and imagination,
I don't think you can go wrong.
ELLA FITZGERALD

I am grateful for...

1. _____
2. _____
3. _____

What would make today great?

1. _____
2. _____
3. _____

Daily affirmation

_____
_____

Highlights of the Day

1. _____
2. _____
3. _____

What did I learn today?

_____
_____

_......... / .... / 20 ......_

The good life is built with good relationships.
ROBERT WALDINGER

I am grateful for...

1. _____
2. _____
3. _____

What would make today great?

1. _____
2. _____
3. _____

Daily affirmation

_____

_____

Highlights of the Day

1. _____
2. _____
3. _____

What did I learn today?

_____

_____

Sometimes what you're looking for is already there.
ARETHA FRANKLIN

I am grateful for...

1. _____
2. _____
3. _____

What would make today great?

1. _____
2. _____
3. _____

Daily affirmation

_____
_____

Highlights of the Day

1. _____
2. _____
3. _____

What did I learn today?

_____
_____

WEEKLY CHALLENGE

A dish that I want to try cooking is _____. Invite friends over and prepare it together. Share this experience with them.

I am grateful for...

1. _____
2. _____
3. _____

What would make today great?

1. _____
2. _____
3. _____

Daily affirmation

_____
_____

Highlights of the Day

1. _____
2. _____
3. _____

What did I learn today?

_____
_____

The meaning of life is to find your gift.
The purpose of life is to give it away.
PABLO PICASSO

I am grateful for...

1. _____
2. _____
3. _____

What would make today great?

1. _____
2. _____
3. _____

Daily affirmation

_____
_____

Highlights of the Day

1. _____
2. _____
3. _____

What did I learn today?

_____
_____

Give thanks for a little and you will find a lot.
HANSA PROVERB

I am grateful for...

1. _____
2. _____
3. _____

What would make today great?

1. _____
2. _____
3. _____

Daily affirmation

_____

_____

Highlights of the Day

1. _____
2. _____
3. _____

What did I learn today?

_____

_____

Every morning we get a chance to be different.
A chance to change. A chance to be better.
NICOLE WILLIAMS

I am grateful for...

1. _____
2. _____
3. _____

What would make today great?

1. _____
2. _____
3. _____

Daily affirmation

_____

_____

Highlights of the Day

1. _____
2. _____
3. _____

What did I learn today?

_____

_____

A gentle word, a kind look, a good-natured smile
can work wonders and accomplish miracles.
WILLIAM HAZLITT

I am grateful for...

1. _____
2. _____
3. _____

What would make today great?

1. _____
2. _____
3. _____

Daily affirmation

_____
_____

Highlights of the Day

1. _____
2. _____
3. _____

What did I learn today?

_____
_____

*All we have to decide is what to do with the time
that is given to us.*

J. R. R. TOLKIEN

I am grateful for...

1. _____
2. _____
3. _____

What would make today great?

1. _____
2. _____
3. _____

Daily affirmation

_____
_____

Highlights of the Day

1. _____
2. _____
3. _____

What did I learn today?

_____
_____

WEEKLY CHALLENGE

*Give or send your parents (or any other close family member)
a small gift without any reason, just to show your love and
appreciation, just to make them smile.*

I am grateful for...

1. _____
2. _____
3. _____

What would make today great?

1. _____
2. _____
3. _____

Daily affirmation

_____
_____

Highlights of the Day

1. _____
2. _____
3. _____

What did I learn today?

_____
_____

Don't judge each day by the harvest you reap,
but by the seeds you plant.

ROBERT LOUIS STEVENSON

I am grateful for...

1. _____
2. _____
3. _____

What would make today great?

1. _____
2. _____
3. _____

Daily affirmation

_____
_____

Highlights of the Day

1. _____
2. _____
3. _____

What did I learn today?

_____
_____

Good things take time.
JOHN WOODEN

I am grateful for...

1. _____
2. _____
3. _____

What would make today great?

1. _____
2. _____
3. _____

Daily affirmation

_____

_____

Highlights of the Day

1. _____
2. _____
3. _____

What did I learn today?

_____

_____

Reminder

You have two weeks of the journal left to complete.

We recommend that you order your next
Five Minute Journal from our website:

GET 10% OFF your purchase
CODE: GRATITUDE
intelligentchange.com

Nothing can bring you happiness but yourself.
RALPH WALDO EMERSON

I am grateful for...

1. _____
2. _____
3. _____

What would make today great?

1. _____
2. _____
3. _____

Daily affirmation

_____

_____

Highlights of the Day

1. _____
2. _____
3. _____

What did I learn today?

_____

_____

Every next level of your life will demand a different you.
LEONARDO DICAPRIO

I am grateful for...

1. _____
2. _____
3. _____

What would make today great?

1. _____
2. _____
3. _____

Daily affirmation

_____
_____

Highlights of the Day

1. _____
2. _____
3. _____

What did I learn today?

_____
_____

236

The measure of success is happiness and peace of mind.
BOBBY DAVRO

I am grateful for...

1. _____
2. _____
3. _____

What would make today great?

1. _____
2. _____
3. _____

Daily affirmation

_____
_____

Highlights of the Day

1. _____
2. _____
3. _____

What did I learn today?

_____
_____

237

*Create the highest, grandest vision possible for
your life, because you become what you believe.*

OPRAH WINFREY

I am grateful for...

1. _____
2. _____
3. _____

What would make today great?

1. _____
2. _____
3. _____

Daily affirmation

_____

_____

Highlights of the Day

1. _____
2. _____
3. _____

What did I learn today?

_____

_____

Your positive action combined with positive thinking
results in success.

SHIV KHERA

I am grateful for...

1. _____

2. _____

3. _____

What would make today great?

1. _____

2. _____

3. _____

Daily affirmation

_____

_____

Highlights of the Day

1. _____

2. _____

3. _____

What did I learn today?

_____

_____

My future starts when I wake up in the morning.
Every day I find something creative to do with my life.
MILES DAVIS

I am grateful for...

1. _____
2. _____
3. _____

What would make today great?

1. _____
2. _____
3. _____

Daily affirmation

_____
_____

Highlights of the Day

1. _____
2. _____
3. _____

What did I learn today?

_____
_____

240

WEEKLY CHALLENGE

Things that uplift me are _____.
Do one today.

I am grateful for...

1. _____
2. _____
3. _____

What would make today great?

1. _____
2. _____
3. _____

Daily affirmation

_____

_____

Highlights of the Day

1. _____
2. _____
3. _____

What did I learn today?

_____

_____

Gratitude turns what we have into enough.

AESOP

I am grateful for...

1. _____
2. _____
3. _____

What would make today great?

1. _____
2. _____
3. _____

Daily affirmation

_____

_____

Highlights of the Day

1. _____
2. _____
3. _____

What did I learn today?

_____

_____

242

Act as if what you do makes a difference. It does.
WILLIAM JAMES

I am grateful for...

1. _____
2. _____
3. _____

What would make today great?

1. _____
2. _____
3. _____

Daily affirmation

_____
_____

Highlights of the Day

1. _____
2. _____
3. _____

What did I learn today?

_____
_____

We make living by what we get.
We make a life by what we give.
WINSTON CHURCHILL

I am grateful for...

1. _____
2. _____
3. _____

What would make today great?

1. _____
2. _____
3. _____

Daily affirmation

_____
_____

Highlights of the Day

1. _____
2. _____
3. _____

What did I learn today?

_____
_____

Yesterday is history. Tomorrow is a mystery.
Today is a gift. That's why it is called the present.
ALICE MORSE EARLE

I am grateful for...

1. _____
2. _____
3. _____

What would make today great?

1. _____
2. _____
3. _____

Daily affirmation

_____
_____

Highlights of the Day

1. _____
2. _____
3. _____

What did I learn today?

_____
_____

.... / .... / 20 ......

You change the world by being yourself.

YOKO ONO

I am grateful for...

1. _____
2. _____
3. _____

What would make today great?

1. _____
2. _____
3. _____

Daily affirmation

_____
_____

Highlights of the Day

1. _____
2. _____
3. _____

What did I learn today?

_____
_____

In life, one has a choice to take one of two paths:
to wait for some special day or to celebrate each special day.
RASHEED OGUNLARU

I am grateful for...

1. _____
2. _____
3. _____

What would make today great?

1. _____
2. _____
3. _____

Daily affirmation

_____

_____

Highlights of the Day

1. _____
2. _____
3. _____

What did I learn today?

_____

_____

247

Day by day, what you choose, what you think
and what you do is who you become.

HERACLITUS

I am grateful for...

1. _____
2. _____
3. _____

What would make today great?

1. _____
2. _____
3. _____

Daily affirmation

_____
_____

Highlights of the Day

1. _____
2. _____
3. _____

What did I learn today?

_____
_____

WEEKLY CHALLENGE

Congratulations! You have just finished 6 months of the journal.
Take a few minutes to look back through your entries and
appreciate what you have written.

I am grateful for...

1. _____
2. _____
3. _____

What would make today great?

1. _____
2. _____
3. _____

Daily affirmation

_____

_____

Highlights of the Day

1. _____
2. _____
3. _____

What did I learn today?

_____

_____

249

There's a secret that real writers know that wannabe writers don't, and the secret is this: *It's not the writing part that's hard.* What's hard is sitting down to write. What keeps us from sitting down is *resistance*.

STEVEN PRESSFIELD

Milestones &
Coffee Breaks

Congratulations! You have completed 6 months of The Five Minute Journal. Take a few minutes to reflect and reward yourself for creating a wonderful new habit. You have reached for your journal on days when you were already cozy in bed and suddenly remembered you hadn't filled in your entry.

Bravo on beating resistance on both counts.

Now is the time to take a deep breath, smile, and rest a few moments to celebrate this milestone. Milestones exist for us as barometers for how far we have come and also remind us that the journey surely continues. They allow us to take inventory of the past and plan for the future—just like the beginning of the new year, birthdays, and coffee breaks. Please enjoy this milestone by treating yourself to something nice.

HOW HAS THE FIVE MINUTE JOURNAL CHANGED YOUR LIFE?

We'd love to hear your story!
Email us at hello@intelligentchange.com

We also hope you are ready with your new copy of
the Journal so you can continue writing tomorrow.

GET 10% OFF your purchase
CODE: GRATITUDE
intelligentchange.com

References

1. Why 44% of Doctors are Overweight
Kalb, C. (October 13, 2008) Drop that corn dog, doctor. Newsweek

2. Willpower is a Limited Resource
Baumeister, R. F., Bratslavsky, E., Muraven, M., & Tice, D. M. (1998) Ego depletion: Is the active self a limited resource? Journal of Personality and Social Psychology

3. 5 Hours and 11 Minutes of TV Per Day
A.C. Nielsen Co (2012)
BLS American Time Use Survey

4. Gratitude
Emmons, R.A. and McCullough, M.E. (2003) Counting blessings versus burdens: an experimental investigation of gratitude and subjective well-being in daily life

5. Hypothalamus
Zahn, R. et al (2008) The Neural Basis of Human Social Values: Evidence from Functional MRI

6. Thinking About Watching a Movie
American Physiological Society (April 3, 2006) Just the expectation of a mirthful laughter experience boosts endorphins 27 percent, HGH, 87 percent.

7. Daily Affirmations
Crum A.J. & Langer, E.J. (2007)
Mindset matters: Exercise and the placebo effect. Psychological Science, 18(2)

8. The Bad News
http://www.prnewswire.com/
news-releases/dont-be-among-the-eighty-eight-percent-of-new-years-resolu-tions-that-fail-1126Five4799.html

NOTES

NOTES

NOTES

NOTES

NOTES

NOTES

NOTES